Riddles and Rhymes and Rigmaroles

By the same author

Farmer Barnes Buys a Pig
Farmer Barnes and Bluebell
Farmer Barnes at the County Show
Farmer Barnes and the Goats
The Giant Who Stole the World
The Adventures of Lord Pip

JOHN CUNLIFFE

Riddles and Rhymes and Rigmaroles

Drawings by Alexy Pendle

 ANDRE DEUTSCH

First published 1971 by
André Deutsch Limited
105 Great Russell Street, London WCI

Printed in Great Britain by
Ebenezer Baylis and Son Ltd
The Trinity Press, Worcester, and London

ISBN 0 233 96306 5

Contents

Dear reader

The riddles are also poems. If you cannot answer the riddle, I hope you can enjoy the poem; and vice versa. Anyway, you will find the answers at the end of the book.

The rhymes are a mixture of puzzle-poems, nonsense, jokes and other games with words. Not all of them are meant to be funny.

The rigmaroles are endless tales and other nonsense in prose.

I hope you enjoy them all.

John Cunliffe.

Riddles

Number 1

See it go along the street,
Carried by no human feet,
Town or country, feast or fair,
A crown no king or queen can wear.

Number 2

Some thing I tell,
With never a word;
I keep it well,
Though it flies like a bird.

Number 3

Hold it steady in your hand,
Then you will see another land,
Where right is left, and left is right,
And no sound stirs by day or night;
When you look in, yourself you see,
Yet in that place you cannot be.

Number 4

One can bear it,
Two can share it,
But for three
it never can be.

Number 5

I have no voice and yet I speak to you,
I tell of all things in the world that people do;
I have leaves, but I am not a tree,
I have pages, but I am not a bride or royalty;
I have a spine and hinges, but I am not a man or a
  door,
I have told you all . . . I cannot tell you more.

Number 6

Both day and night I stay in bed,
Yet never sleep or rest my head;
I have no feet to skip or hop,
And yet I run and never stop.

Number 7

In rainy squall or pattering shower,
I open like a sudden flower;
But when the wind blows strong to gale,
I huddle close and furl my sail;
Then, peg-leg hopping down the street,
I follow close my master's feet.

Number 8

A many-tongued monster roared over the hill,
That never, oh never, could eat its fill;
Both houses and trees, it devoured them all,
Then covered the scene with a tattered pall.

12

Number 9   Feet

The foot that pays,
And the foot that plays;
The thieving foot that walks,
And the foot that talks;
The foot that begins a climb,
And the foot that blooms in summertime.

(There is a different answer for each line of the poem.)

Number 10
Airs On A Riddling Theme

A gentle one cools my steaming cup,
A cold one makes the cat curl up,
A stiff one sends my kite up high,
A strong one tempts my hat to fly.

(There is a separate answer for each line.)

Number 11

I begin,
Tall and thin;
I end in a muddle,
Sat in a puddle.

Number 12   Falls

This fall enfolds the drowsy land;
This drops fool or prince in fortune's hand;
This brings the sailor safe from the sea;
This brings wealth where none before could be.

(*There is a separate answer for each line.*)

Number 13

They shrink and grow, or fade and die,
As sun or moon do cross the sky;
And as across my wall they creep,
They fall more silently than sleep.

Number 14

Summer come and summer go,
Here's a ball you can touch, but never throw;
Winter dusk and winter night,
Here's a ball of dark and light;
Splendid spring and ashen Fall,
Gaze you not upon *this* golden ball.

(*There are three answers; one for each couplet.*)

Rhymes

Craster Kippers

Three Craster fishermen set out one day,
To cast their nets beyond the bay,
But alas for Aidan and Andrew and Tim,
Those nets were moth-eaten, their holes wearing thin!
So they lost fifty cod-fish and twenty-two trout.
Says Aidan, 'Lord save us, they're all slipping out!'
They caught fifty herring, but twelve got away.
Says Andrew, 'At this rate we'll ne'er earn our pay!'
But they caught seventy mackerel, of flounders a score,
Two dace, and of whiting a dozen or more.

Now tell me, if you can, I pray,
Of all the fish they caught that day,
How many *kippers* got away?

They sell fresh kippers by the strand,
At Craster in Northumberland,
And it's, 'Kippers! Fresh kippers! Fresh kippers!'
  all day,
But how many kippers got away?

(*The answer to this rhyme is at the back of the book.*)

Doctor Nicholas

One day when I was feeling sick,
I paid a call on Doctor Nick.
Now Doctor Nicholas said to me,
'You must use hair-oil in your tea,
Put plenty of sugar in your ears,
Use cotton-wool when the weather clears,
Take country walks when you go to bed,
Use feather pillows on your bread,
Use butter for your daily dip,
Good soap and water you should sip;
This tonic, for you, I will prescribe,
And if you do as I describe,
Rarely, if ever, will you feel sick.'

'Oh, thank you, thank you, Doctor Nick!'

I took my coat, I went my ways,
And I've been healthy all my days,
I followed the Doctor's word to the letter,
And truth to tell, I never felt better.

(*Can you make sense of the Doctor's instructions?*
Try moving the commas.)

A Birthday to Remember

It was a birthday to remember,
On the third day of November,
When I did reach the age of ten.
The celebrations were sedate,
Till some presents came in late,
From my Indian uncle Ben.

On the first day
Of my birthday,
My uncle sent with heartfelt
    wishes,
A whale and a quail on silver
    dishes!

Silver dishes with heartfelt
    wishes!

On the second day
Of my birthday,
My uncle sent with Happy
    Returns,
A dozen Dead Sea Diggers,
    unearthing unique urns!

Silver dishes with heartfelt
    wishes,
Unique urns with Happy
    Returns!

On the third day
Of my birthday,
My uncle sent with Kind
  Regards,
A pair of Persian Pigs, and a
  bundle of British Bards!

Silver Dishes with Heartfelt
  Wishes,
Unique Urns with Happy
  Returns,
British Bards with Kind
  Regards!

On the fourth day
Of my birthday,
My uncle sent as an
  afterthought,
A laying hen and a four-
  legged goat!

Silver dishes with Heartfelt
  Wishes,
Unique Urns with Happy
  Returns,
British Bards with Kind
  Regards,
A four-legged goat as an
  afterthought!

On the fifth day
Of my birthday,
My uncle sent to wish me well,
A temple tower and a tolling
    bell!

Silver Dishes with Heartfelt
    Wishes,
Unique Urns with Happy
    Returns,
British Bards with Kind
    Regards,
A four-legged goat as an
    afterthought,
A tolling bell to wish me well!

On the sixth day
Of my birthday,
My uncle sent to Wish me
    Luck,
A singing snake and a
    whistling duck!

Silver Dishes with Heartfelt
    Wishes,
Unique Urns with Happy
    Returns,
British Bards with Kind
    Regards,
A four-legged goat as an
    afterthought,

A tolling bell to Wish me Well,
A Whistling Duck to Wish me
    Luck!

On the seventh day
Of my birthday,
My Uncle Ben returned from
    foreign parts,
With Twenty Tons of
    Roumanian Rhubarb in
    Twenty Roumanian
    Rhubarb Carts!

What a birthday to remember,
On that third day of November,
When I reached the tender age
    of ten!
All was peace as I relate,
Till those presents came in late,
From my Indian Uncle Ben.
But never again, no never
    again;
All letters and parcels sent to me
    on that day,
Will be marked,
    'NO ADDRESS – GONE AWAY'!

Never Forget

'Twenty-six letters
In the alphabet.'
My elders and betters
Say, 'Never forget.'

But, A went to play,
And B went to sea,
And C went to Fiji,
So that left only twenty-three.

Then D had to flee,
And E went to ski,
And F became deaf,
So that left only twenty
To learn, and that's plenty.

But G went out to tea,
And H went to preach,
And I swallowed a fly,
So only seventeen remain,
To tease my brain.

But J was carried away,
And K sailed to Bombay,
Where L went to dwell.
That leaves fourteen letters,
To repeat for my betters.

But M donned a diadem,
And N took up Zen,
So O had to go,
Leaving only eleven in hand,
To understand.

But P climbed a tree,
And Q fell in the stew,
And R went too far;
Leaving only eight,
To prate.

But S joined the press,
And T went on a spree,
And U joined a crew;
Leaving only five,
So we'll soon arrive.

Then V was stung by a bee,
And W said, 'I'll not fuddle you,'
So XYZ went to bed;
None remain to puzzle my wits,
I've disposed of them all by starts and fits.

This rhyme I say,
Each day,
To my betters,
So that I'll never need to learn my letters.

Pot and Pan

Little old lady and man,
Lived in a pot and pan.
When the pan fried and the sun did shine,
He rode proudly out to dine;
When the cool winds blew and the pot was hot,
She took her dappled mare for a trot.

When pot and pan were on together,
They both went out in *any* weather.

I Once Saw An Ant

I once saw an ant as big as a mouse,
Running and scratching about my house;
I once saw a mouse as big as a cat,
That mewed and chewed inside an old hat;
I once saw a cat as big as a pig,
That ate an old apple, three pears and a fig;
I once saw a pig as big as a cow,
That knew how to curtsey but not how to bow;
I once saw a cow as big as a whale,
That never gave milk, but only brown ale;
I once saw a whale, I once saw a whale . . .
Nothing is bigger, and so ends my tale.

Dog Days

Monday's dog is as fat as a hog,
Tuesday's dog gets lost in the fog,
Wednesday's dog is long in the tail,
Thursday's dog drinks good ale,
Friday's dog is rather *dog-eared*,
Saturday's dog is often afeared,
Sunday's dog sits on the mat,
Watching the television cat.

Some curious creatures

(i) THE APOLOGETIC ASS

The apologetic ass,
Put out to grass,
Watches clouds and people pass.

(ii) THE FASTIDIOUS FLEA

The fastidious flea,
Bit *you* at tea,
But wouldn't take even a nibble from me.

(iii) THE FRUGAL FLY

The frugal fly investigates,
All about my dinner plates;
A crumb that I can hardly see,
Makes a feast for such as he.

(iv) THE WANDERING WORM

The wandering worm spends all day,
Coiling through a clod of clay;
Clay he digs and eats and drinks,
Only of clay – all day – he thinks.

Gnu?

I'm a gnu,
In a zoo.
Who
Are you?

Garbled Nursery Rhymes

(i) JACK HORNER AND HIS MOTHER

'Little Jack Horner,
Sat in the corner . . .'

> *'Your name isn't Horner
> at all; you've just put
> that in for the rhyme,'
> said his mother.*

'Little Jack Abel,
Sat in the corner . . .'

> *'Why do you sit in that
> dark corner,' grumbled
> Mother. 'Sit up at table
> properly to eat.'*

'Little Jack Abel,
Sat at the table,
Eating a Christmas
    pie; . . .'

> *'That's no pie. It's a flan.'*

'Little Jack Abel,
Sat at the table,
Eating a Christmas
    flan; . . .'

> *'It isn't Christmas.'*

'Little Jack Abel,
Sat at the table,
Eating a midsummer
    flan;
He put in his thumb . . . '

*'For goodness sake, child,
use your spoon. It's
most unhygienic to put
your thumb in your
food.'*

'Little Jack Abel,
Sat at the table,
Eating a midsummer flan;
He put in his spoon,
And pulled out a
    plum . . .'

*'You cannot pull a plum
out of a strawberry
flan.'*

'Little Jack Abel,
Sat at the table,
Eating a midsummer flan;
He put in his spoon,
And pulled out a
    prune . . .'

*'No. No. No. You cannot
pull a prune out of a
strawberry flan, either.'*

'Little Jack Abel,
Sat at the table,
Eating a midsummer flan;
He put in his spoon,
Like a silly buffoon,

*And ate three strawberries, and quickly, before his
mother could get another word in, he slipped in the
final rhyme,*

And said, What a good boy I am!'

(ii) THE GRAND OLD DUKE OF PISA

(*With acknowledgements to Julian Cunliffe.*)

The Grand Old Duke of Pisa,
He had ten thousand peas,
He rolled them up and down the hill,
As often as he did please;
And when they were up they were up,
And when they were down they were down,
And when they were only half way up,
They were reduced to pease-pudding, which he put
in small bowls and gave to
hungry people in the town.

(iii)

Humpty Dumpty sat on a wall,
Humpty Dumpty had a great fall,
He didn't break at all . . .
He was hard-boiled!

(iv)

Mary had a little lamb,
Its fleece was white as snow;
She wound it up with a great big key,
And that's what made it go.

There was an old woman who lived in a shoe,
She had so many children she must know what to do;
She made them rise early, for she was no fool,
Then washed their faces and sent them to school.

(vi)

Hickory Dickory Dock,
The mouse ran up the clock,
The clock struck one,
And another one,
And another one,
And another one,
Right on the mouse's head.
'I'm sick of your running up and down,' it said,
And killed the mouse stone dead!

Odd Outing

I went out to tea one morning,
As the moon was shining bright,
The day was fine and pouring,
So I stayed till the previous night.

Playing With Puns

(i)

One day they locked me up in jail,
For drinking more than I should of ale;
Snapping my fingers, with a crack, crack, crack,
I crept through a crack, and never came back.

(ii)

One day I went with high ambition,
To enter a fishing competition;
I didn't get a bite, not so much as a snail,
So I began to weep and wail;
That whale was more than average size,
So I walked away with the biggest prize!

(iii)

Walking along the road one day,
Who should I meet but Farmer Grey;
There he stood as cross as a witch,
For his old Ford car was stuck in a ditch.
I yelled and shouted till I was horse,
And we galloped home across the gorse.

I Saw Two Pigs

I saw two pigs bake a pie,
I saw a girl spread wings and fly,
I saw a swan beating a drum,
I saw a man the size of my thumb,
I saw a nut go to the moon,
I saw a space-ship as big as a spoon,
I saw a fork that told a tale,
I saw a book as big as a whale,
I saw a ship upon the sea,
And all these things you too may see.

*(This is another punctuation puzzle. Move the commas,
and see if you can make sense of it.)*

A Very Strange Journey

One day I felt seasick on the bus,
'Oh,' said the pilot, 'don't make a fuss,
This train can swim as fast as a snail.'
So I ate a slice of beer and ale.

Soon I began to feel better and better,
So I went to the telephone to send a letter.
'I cannot see you,' the operator said,
So I woke myself up and went to bed.

Piece of String

Piece of string,
Piece of string,
What can you do
with a piece of string?

If it's loose,
Make a noose;
If it's loose,
Make a noose.

If it tangles,
Make some bangles;
If it tangles,
Make some bangles.

Piece of string,
Piece of string,
What can you do
with a piece of string?

If it whirls,
Make some curls;
If it whirls,
Make some curls.

If you drop it,
Swop it;
If you drop it,
Swop it.

Piece of string,
Piece of string,
What can you do
with a piece of string?

If it snags,
Make some bags;
If it snags,
Make some bags.

If it's long,
Catch a dugong;
If it's long,
Catch a dugong.

If it's tight,
Make a kite;
If it's tight,
Make a kite.

If it's knotted,
Eat it potted;
If it's knotted,
Eat it potted.

If it's frayed,
Make some braid;
If it's frayed,
Make some braid.

So I sing,
So I sing,
You can do most
    anything,
With a simple piece of
    string.

The Flower of Happiness

This is the flower of happiness,
That grows in a meadow,
That is in a valley,
That is in a land,
That is by a sea,
That is in an ocean,
That is in a world,
That is in a dream,
Dreamed by a girl,
Who is in a bed;
The bed is in a room,
The room is in a house,
The house is in a street,
The street is in a town,
The town is in a land,
The land is by a sea,
The sea is in an ocean,
The ocean is in a world,
Wherein the flower of happiness grows,
In a meadow,
That is in a valley,
That is in a land,
That is by a sea,
That is in an ocean,
That is in a world,
That is in a dream,
Dreamed by a girl,
Who is in a bed;
The bed is in a room,
The room is in a house . . .
    (and so on, and on, for ever.)

43

Bird Song

The bird in the tree,
And the tree in the wood;
The heart in me,
And the song in the blood.

Fish Song

The fish in the stream,
And the stream on the hill;
The heart's flowing dream,
And the quick-swimming will.

The Magic Fish

The magic fish it glides and gleams,
Through the darkness of my dreams;
It glows where none has gone before,
Swimming by a distant shore.

What Can You Do?

What can you do,
With a single shoe?
Give it to . . .
A gnu.

What can you do,
With a single glove?
Give it to . . .
The one you love.

What can you do,
With a single knicker?
Give it to . . .
The vicar.

What can you do,
With a single trouser?
Give it to . . .
A water-dowser.

What can you do,
With a single spectacle?
Give it to . . .
A person who possesses
    a suitable receptacle.

What can you do,
With a single scissor?
Give it to . . .
A miser.

What can you do,
With a single shear?
Give it to . . .
A man of good cheer.

What can you do,
With a single sock?
Give it to . . .
A cold-tailed cock.

What can you do,
With a single tong?
Give it to . . .
A man in Hong Kong

What can you do,
With a single slipper?
Give it to . . .
A day-tripper.

Growing

When I was one,
I had a scone;
When I was two,
A pot of glue;
When I was three,
A day by the sea;
When I was four,
The faery lore;
When I was five,
A cat alive;
When I was six,
A cake to mix;
When I was seven,
A trip to Devon;
When I was eight,
A left-hand skate;
When I was nine,
A celandine;
When I was ten,
I went among men.

Rigmaroles

The Man and the Bear

A man was walking in a wild wood, and he met a bear. The bear growled and said,

'I am going to eat you up.'

The man said,

'Wait a minute. Let me tell you a story before you eat me.'

'I *love* stories,' said the bear, 'sit down on this rock and begin.' So the man and the bear sat down together on a smooth rock nearby, and the man began his story.

'Once upon a time,' he said, 'a man was walking in a wild wood and he met a bear. The bear growled, and said, "I am going to eat you up." The man said, "Wait a minute. Let me tell you a story before you eat me." "I *love* stories," said the bear, "sit down on this rock and begin." So the man and the bear sat down together on a smooth rock nearby, and the man began his story.'

'Once upon a time,' he said, 'a man was walking in a wild wood and he met a bear. The bear growled, and said, "I am going to eat you up." The man said, "Wait a minute. Let me tell you a story before you eat me." "I *love* stories," said the bear, "sit down on this rock and begin." So the man and the bear sat down together on a smooth rock nearby, and the man began his story.'

'Once upon a time,' he said, 'a man was walking in a wild wood, and he met a bear. The bear growled and said, "I am going to eat you up." The man said, "Wait a minute. Let me tell you a story . . ."'

The bear yawned, and held up a paw.

'It seems a very *long* story. When does it end?' he asked.

'I cannot tell you that,' said the man. 'It would spoil the whole story.'

'Then I cannot eat you yet,' said the bear, 'for I cannot bear a story to be left unfinished. You'd better go on.' And he settled down to listen.
The man went on with his story –

'. . . before you eat me. "I *love* stories," said the bear. "Sit down on this rock and begin." So the man and the bear sat down together on a smooth rock nearby, and the man began his story.

'Once upon a time,' he said, 'a man was walking in a wild wood and he met a bear. The bear growled. . . .'

The story went on and on and on and on and on and on and on and on. It went on from dinner-time to tea-time; from tea-time to supper-time. The bear's head began to nod. He fell fast asleep. The silly creature didn't guess that the story had no ending! The man stopped telling his story. He quietly tiptoed away, leaving the bear to his slumber. His endless story had saved him from being eaten.

Now if *you* should meet a hungry bear that likes stories, you will know what to do.

Julian's Bed

Once there was a boy called Julian who was making his bed. He smoothed the sheets and blankets, puffed the pillow up and tucked everything in. It was bed-time, so he undressed and got into his bed. This untucked the sheets and blankets and rumpled them; his head squashed the pillow.

'Oh dear,' he said to himself, 'now I've unmade my bed.' So Julian got out of bed and made his bed again. He smoothed the sheets and blankets, puffed up the pillow and tucked everything in. It was bed-time, so he undressed and got into his bed. This untucked the sheets and blankets and rumpled them; his head squashed the pillow.

'Oh dear,' he said to himself, 'now I've unmade my bed.' So Julian got out of bed and made his bed again. He smoothed the sheets . . .

The Boy Who Dreamed

There was a boy who dreamed that he was in a beautiful garden. He walked through the garden until he came to a house with a thousand rooms. He opened the door and walked in. He walked through all the thousand rooms; in the last one he found a bed. He lay down and went to sleep. He dreamed that he was in a beautiful garden. He walked through the garden until he came to a house with a thousand rooms. He opened the door and walked in. He walked through all the thousand rooms; in the last one he found a bed. He lay down and went to sleep. He dreamed that he was in a beautiful garden. He walked through the garden . . .

(This is an endless story, like the one that the man told to the bear. If you tell it to your friends, you can go on and on and on with it, until they beg you to stop!)

The Hunter and the Tiger

There was a hunter walking through the jungle, and he met a snarling tiger coming towards him on the path. He reached for his gun. To his horror, he saw that he had no bullets! The tiger was coming nearer. It was going to attack!

'What can I do? I'm going to be eaten up,' thought the hunter, terror freezing him on the spot. Just as the tiger was about to spring, the hunter had a strange feeling.

'I do believe all this is only a dream,' he said. 'If I try hard enough, I'm sure I'll waken up.'

So he pinched himself hard, and shook himself and blinked. In a moment, the tiger was gone; the hunter was safe in his own bed. What a relief! He still trembled with fright. How real that tiger had seemed. Thank goodness it was only a dream.

When he felt calm again, the hunter got up and made himself a cup of tea. He still felt tired, so he sat outside his hut in a deck-chair and smoked his pipe for a while. He really felt quite sleepy. So he tipped his hat over his face, and closed his eyes.

'I could sleep all day,' he said.

After a time, he heard growling.

'Bless me,' said the hunter, 'I must have dropped off to sleep again. There's that tiger coming back. Go away you silly tiger, I'm tired of dreaming about you!'

The tiger growled again, and came nearer.

'I'm not afraid of you. You're only a dream,' said the hunter. Then he got up from his chair, walked up to the tiger, and punched it hard on the nose.

'What a funny man,' thought the tiger. 'Men usually run away from me.'

Then the tiger ate the hunter up, and very good he was, too.

The Whatsit

A man walked into an ironmonger's shop one day. He was holding his hand stiffly at an odd angle, with his thumb and first finger making a small ring.

'Have you got a whatsit, just this size?' he asked the Ironmonger.

'Exactly *what* do you mean by a *whatsit*?' said the Ironmonger scornfully.

'Well, you know,' said the man, 'it goes on a thing-ummy, and holds the doodle-flap on the joggly thing that works the thing that pops when it gets too hot.'

'I don't know what you're talking about,' said the Ironmonger, 'but I'll tell you what we'll do, we'll go and ask my friend the Blacksmith. He's clever with mechanical things. He may know what you mean.' So the Ironmonger put on his coat, and they went out together.

'Be careful not to nudge me, or joggle me, or jiggle me,' said the man. 'If my finger moves even a fraction, I'll lose the size of the whatsit.'

'Don't worry,' said the Ironmonger, 'we have worries enough; I'll not joggle you.'

The man and the Ironmonger walked into the Black-smith's forge, the man holding his hand at the same odd angle.

'Morning, Bill!' said the Ironmonger. 'We have a little problem here, and I thought you might be able to help.'

'It's a pleasure,' said the Blacksmith. 'Nothing mechanical can be a puzzle to me. Now what's the problem?'

'This man wants a sort of . . . well, a kind of . . . *you* know, one of those. . . . *You* tell him,' said the Ironmonger to the man, nudging him, so that he almost moved his finger.

'Careful,' said the man, 'I warned you about nudging. Well, what I want is quite simple, really. I want a whatsit that goes on a thingummy, and holds the doodle-flap on the joggly thing that pops when it's too hot, and it's just *this* size.' He held up his hand, with the thumb and finger crooked into a awkward circle. The Blacksmith scratched his head and looked worried and said,

'Now you really have me there; I've never heard of such a thing. All my life I've mended machines and tools, and made spare-parts that no one could get anywhere else, but never have I heard of the thing you want. I'll tell you what we'll do, though; we'll go and see my friend the Watchmaker. He'll know what your whatsit's all about; he's a real fiend for funny mechanical devices.'

So the Blacksmith put his coat on, and they all went up the road together to the Watchmaker's shop, the man, and the Ironmonger, and the Blacksmith.

'Be careful not to nudge me, or joggle me, or jiggle me,' said the man, who still held his hand stiffly, with his thumb and finger making the same small circle. 'If my finger moves even a fraction, I'll lose the size of the whatsit.'

'Don't worry,' said the Ironmonger and the Blacksmith, 'we have worries enough; we'll not joggle you.'

The man, and the Ironmonger, and the Blacksmith crowded into the Watchmaker's shop, the man holding his hand carefully at the same odd angle.

'Good morning, Charles!' said the Blacksmith. 'We have a problem here that's beaten me, and I thought you'd be just the man to ask.'

'I never thought to see *you* flummoxed,' said the Watchmaker, looking pleased. 'But you've come to the right man if it's a mechanical device you want to know about. I'll be glad to solve your problem. Now, what is the trouble?'

'This man wants one of those . . . well, it's a kind of . . . as you might say . . . not a gasket or a sprocket, but a, a . . . *You* tell him,' said the Blacksmith to the man, nudging him rather hard, so that he almost, *almost*, moved his finger.

'Careful,' said the man, 'I warned you about nudging, and my finger nearly did move then. Well, what I want is quite simple, really. I want a whatsit that goes on a thingummy, and holds the doodle-flap on the joggly thing that pops when it's too hot, and it's just this size.' He held up his hand, with the thumb and finger crooked into an awkward circle.

The Watchmaker rubbed his nose, and looked cross.

'That really is a new one to me. I'm not at all sure . . .' and he disappeared into his back room, and a sound of rummaging and scrabbling could be heard for some time, with a great deal of muttered swearing and cursing, and a dropping of boxes and slamming of doors. He came back at last, looking dusty and muddled, and said,

'I cannot find anything near it. Never did I know such a thing, and I never will. The only thing to do is to go and ask my friend the Librarian. He has a lot of books about machines and all manner of things, encyclopedias and dictionaries and glossaries and what not. He'll be able to tell us, if anyone can, just what this fellow's whatsit is, and where he can get one.'

So the Watchmaker put his coat on, and they all went into town together to the Public Library; the man, and the Ironmonger, and the Blacksmith and the Watchmaker.

'Be careful not to nudge me, or joggle me, or jiggle me,' said the man, who still held his hand stiffly, with his thumb and finger making the same small circle. 'If my finger moves even a fraction, I'll lose the size of the whatsit.'

'Don't worry,' said the Ironmonger, and the Blacksmith and the Watchmaker; 'we have worries enough; we'll not joggle you.'

The man, and the Ironmonger, and the Blacksmith and the Watchmaker trooped into the Public Library, the man holding his hand carefully at the same odd angle.

'Good afternoon, Mr Baily,' said the Watchmaker. 'I do hope you can help us, please. We have a problem here that's beaten all of us, and I reckon you can find the answer if anyone can.'

'We've never failed to answer an inquiry yet,' said the Librarian, smiling confidently. There were rows and rows of books all round him, full of answers to questions. 'What is it that you want to know?'

The Watchmaker said,

'It's this gentleman here; he wishes to know where he can get a . . . one of those . . . the kind of component you need for a . . . Oh, *you* tell him!' giving

61

the man a good nudge, so that he very nearly moved his finger.

'Oh do be careful,' said the man, 'I have warned you about nudging. Well, what I want is quite simple, really. I want a whatsit that goes on a thingummy, and holds the doodle-flap on the joggly thing that pops when it's too hot, and it's just this size.' He held up his hand, with the thumb and finger crooked into an awkward circle. The Librarian had just picked up a large encyclopedia, but he thumped it down on his desk, and began to turn the pages quickly with a deepening frown.

'Would you say that again?' he asked. 'I'm not sure that I heard all those technical terms.'

The man said, 'Yes, all I want is a whatsit that goes on a thingummy, and holds the doodle-flap on the joggly thing that pops when it's too hot, and it's just this size.'

'Yes, that's what I *thought* you said,' said the Librarian with a sigh, and he began pulling book after book from the shelves, more and more quickly. Then he brought a ladder, and climbed to the highest shelves, bringing down fat and ancient volumes, as well as large clouds of dust. Several of the people reading in the library began to sneeze, and a number who had been sleeping peacefully woke up and gazed in astonishment at the commotion. Then the Librarian began telephoning, repeating the man's description of the whatsit each time. No one seemed to be able to help. He even tried the Science Museum in London, and a Dr Urquhart at Boston Spa; but it was no use, no one knew. The Librarian looked a little flushed.

'I'm terribly sorry,' he said, 'but I cannot answer

your question. I've tried everything and everyone, but you have us beaten for the first time in the history of this library!' He looked so sad that they all felt sorry for him, and turned quietly towards the door.

'Wait!' cried the Librarian, wakening all the sleepers again. 'There's one last chance. It may belong to a very old piece of machinery. There's a junk yard not far from here where you can get anything from a model "T" Ford to a gas-fired flat iron. I often get parts for my old car there. My friend Alf runs it, and I feel sure he'd find what you want, even if he cannot put a name to it. He's not on the telephone, so we'll go and see him.'

So the Librarian put his coat on, and they all went out together; the man, and the Ironmonger, and the Blacksmith, and the Watchmaker and the Librarian.

'Be careful not to nudge me, or joggle me, or jiggle me,' said the man, who still held his hand stiffly, with his thumb and finger making the same small circle. 'If my finger moves even a fraction, I'll lose the size of the whatsit.'

'Don't worry,' said the Ironmonger, and the Blacksmith, and the Watchmaker and the Librarian; 'We have worries enough; we'll not joggle you.'

When they reached the junk yard, the man, and the Ironmonger, and the Blacksmith, and the Watchmaker, and the Librarian, picked their way amongst mounds of junk of every description – old cars, washing-machines, penny-farthing bicycles, piles of rusting wheels; buckets of old nails and screws; tubs full of sprockets and gaskets; boxes of magnets, motors and coils; huts full to the roof of old television sets, radios, telephones, telegraphs, semaphores and signals, gadgets and gimmicks. As they searched, the man still held his hand stiffly at the same odd angle, keeping his

finger and thumb fixed firmly to the size of the whatsit.

'Surely we'll find a whatsit somewhere amongst this lot,' he said.

At last, the Librarian caught sight of Alf, and called and called until he climbed down from a mountain of old bath-tubs and came over to them.

'Alf, do come and help us,' said the Librarian. 'I've never known you to fail me, and none of us can find one. You see, this man wants a whatsit that goes on a thingummy, and holds the doodle-flap on the joggly thing that pops when it's too hot . . .'

'And it's just *this* size,' said the man, holding his hand up. 'And you'll have to be quick, too. My hand's getting terribly stiff, and I think I'm going to get a cramp, then I'll *have* to move my finger!'

'Yes, I've got one of those,' said Alf, not hurrying at all. Alf never hurried. 'Mind you, it's the last one. They haven't made them for twenty or thirty years.

I dare say mine's the last one left, anywhere. I've got it in the office safe for safety; they're very fragile. I just hope it's the right size. Now don't move that finger, and I'll get it in a jiffy.'

Alf went off, picking his way along a narrow and junk-cluttered path. The man's hand was beginning to hurt now – he had held it still and stiff for so long.

'I can't hold on much longer; the cramp's coming on,' he said. 'I do wish he'd hurry!'

The others encouraged him. 'Hold on, old fellow,' they said; 'We're nearly there, now.'

'Yes, I can see Alf coming,' said the Librarian. 'And he's carrying something in his hand. Now *don't move that finger*. Hold it! One more minute. Hurry, he's got cramp pains!' he shouted to Alf. At this, Alf did speed up slightly. They could all see something shiny in his hand. How exciting it was, the prospect of seeing this mysterious object at long last! Just then, Alf tripped over a piece of piping. The whatsit flew out of his hand, struck a block of concrete, and shattered into tiny pieces. Alf sat in the middle of the path, looking foolish.

'Well, that's that,' he said. 'The last whatsit in the world – smashed to bits.'

'Oh no!' cried the man. 'No, no, no!' And he sat down, and burst into tears, rubbing and shaking his sore hand.

'After all that trouble,' said the Ironmonger.

'What a waste of time,' said the Blacksmith.

'I could have mended a dozen watches whilst we've been traipsing about,' said the Watchmaker.

'At least we can all find out just *what* this whatsit is, or was,' said the Librarian. 'Do tell us, Alf, we're all dying to know.'

'That's simple,' said Alf, 'it was just a whatsit that goes on a thingummy, and holds the doodle-flap on the joggly thing that pops when it gets . . .'

'Not again! No, no – stop, stop,' they all yelled, and collapsed into helpless, almost hysterical, laughter. The people buying junk crowded round to ask what the joke was, but no one could, or would, tell them!

The Strange Record

William McWilliam put a record on the record-player It began to play.

There was a sound of drums. Violins played a distant dream-tune. Then the music faded, and a voice said,

'William McWilliam put a record on the record-player.
It began to play.
There was a sound of drums. Violins played a distant dream-tune. Then the music faded, and a voice said,

'William McWilliam put a record on the record-player. It began to play. There was a sound of drums. Violins played a distant dream-tune. Then the music faded, and a voice said,

"William McWilliam put a record. . . ." '

'STOP!' cried William McWilliam.

'STOP. STOP. Stop. Stop. Stop. stop. stop. stop. . . .' cried a multitude of voices; echoing, echoing, far far away into the distance.

Mrs Gittipin's Recipe

In taking down a recipe, Mrs Gittipin got all her full-stops and commas in the wrong places. This was the result.

Take three eggs with a handle.
Take a pan and warm in the oven till soft.
Half-a-pound of butter throw away.
Any eggs that are bad you should use.
Salt and pepper, add three dessert-spoons.
Of milk – use the best, and beat all the ingredients together.
Serve.
Piping hot guests will enjoy this dish in summer or winter.

(It is strange enough to have a story without any ending, but what about a story without any beginning either? Here is one. Perhaps you can make more up for yourself?)

The River

. . . into the river. He thought it would be deep, but it was not. It only came up to his knees. So Jimmy trailed his net through the dark weeds, and caught some quick silver fish. He put them in his jar, but it seemed cruel to keep them swimming round in such a narrow tunnel of water. 'Oh, Oh, Oh,' they seemed to say, in dismay. So he let them go. Flick, splash; they were gone. Then Jimmy walked to the edge and jumped . . .

The Weird Record

Colin put a record on the record-player.
He put the needle on the record.
Scratch. Scratch.   Scratch. Scratch.

A voice said,
   'Take it off. That needle's scratching me!'

Colin took the needle off.

   'That's better,' said the voice. 'Now switch me off.
I'm sleepy.'

Colin switched the record-player off.

   'Thank you,' said the voice. 'Good-night.'

Old Mother Turvey and her Pig

(This is a drawing - story. *You should draw the picture as you tell the story.)*

Old Mother Turvey lived in a cottage near a big hill, and she kept a pig in her garden. She wore an apron, like this –

One day, the postman left the garden gate open, and the pig ran away. Off went Old Mother Turvey after it. First, she ran over the hill –

She still couldn't see her pig, but the wind blew so hard that her apron came undone, and the strings blew about, all twisted and tangled –

Off she went again, round the corner of the lane

Until she came to Farmer Tribe's well.

'Has my poor old pig fallen down the well?' she said to herself. And she looked down and down, to see –

She couldn't see it there, so she went to look in Farmer Salt's well too –

There was no sign of it there either, so she ran into the valley –

And the poor old soul fell and slipped into a hole in the ground –

And no sooner was she up, than she was down again –

Then she went round by Pearson's Corner, and peered into a deep dark cave –

But she only saw a barrel with two holes in it –

So she went home, and there she found her old pig waiting for her!

Andrew the Astronaut

(*Another* drawing - story)

Once there was an astronaut called Andrew.
He left his space-ship and went for a moon-walk.
He walked so far across the moon that he got lost. He
could not see his space-ship anywhere, and he couldn't
get home without it. His friends were orbiting over-
head. So that they would see him, he began writing
his name in the moon-dust, with his feet. He began
with a big 'A', like this –

He got tired of doing this, so he thought he would walk
a little further, like this –

On the way, he passed a crater, like this –

The sun was shining in his face and dazzling him, so he turned to one side, like this —

But then he came to a high cliff that he could not climb, so he had to turn back, like this —

Now he saw a lot of big boulders, and he jumped over them all, one after another, like this —

Then he climbed a steep hill, like this –

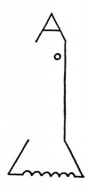

He saw his 'A', and made for it as fast as he could –

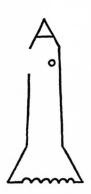

Passing another crater on the way –

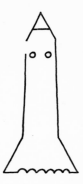

When he reached it, he suddenly saw his space-ship –

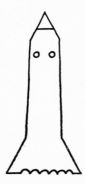

It had been there all the time, waiting to take him home!

Answers to the Riddles

The four drawings which Alexy Pendle made for the riddles are not really meant to be clues; she thought that wouldn't be quite fair. She drew the creatures and people as she saw them in her imagination when she first read the poems and stories in the book.

1. The *crown* of the road.

   Alexy Pendle writes: 'This creature has fins instead of human feet. On his head is a crown of fire which no king or queen could wear without being unpleasantly burnt. He has with him a cat, a bird and a lobster. They are there to make the picture more interesting.'

2. A clock. It *tells* the time, and a good clock will *keep* good time, even though time is always passing.

3. A mirror.

4. A secret.

5. A book.

6. A river.

7. An umbrella.

8. A forest-fire.

   'The monster has just roared over the hill. His scales are made of glowing embers and his tongue and spines are flames. Behind him you can see the blackened stumps of trees, and he is now preparing to destroy a village. His wings are made of smoke and soot and charcoal, they smell very foul.' That is how Alexy Pendle imagines a forest fire.

9. Foot the bill; football; footpad; footnote; a hill's foot; coltsfoot.

10. A breath; a draught; a breeze; wind.
11. A candle.

> Alexy Pendle thought of the candle as being a man. She says: 'The man is so tall and thin that whenever he tries to stand up he immediately collapses. The puddle in which he is sitting is very muddy.'

12. Nightfall; downfall; landfall; windfall.
13. Shadows.
14. The earth; the moon; the sun.

Answer to 'Craster Kippers'

None. No *kippers* could get away, because there are no kippers in the sea! When a herring is caught, then it is smoked, and only then is it called a kipper.

Now you know the answer you know that there are no kippers in the sea. So Alexy Pendle did not draw 'cod, trout, mackerel, herring or any of the real fish mentioned in John Cunliffe's rhyme.' Instead she drew imaginary fishes, some of which had seen the net and were being very careful not to get caught.